The ORGAN WORKS of

J. S. BACH

BOOK XVI

THE SIX "SCHÜBLER" CHORALE PRELUDES

AND

THE "CLAVIERÜBUNG," PART III

With an Introduction by Ernest Newman

NOVELLO

Borough Green   Sevenoaks   Kent TN15 8DT

PRINTED IN GREAT BRITAIN

INTRODUCTION.

THE chorale prelude (or its congener the chorale variation) runs through the whole of Bach's artistic life. At the age of eighteen or so he wrote, either at Lüneberg (1700-1703) or at Arnstadt (1704-1706) the chorale partitas [1] on the melodies of *Christ, der du bist der helle Tag, O Gott, du frommer Gott,* and *Sei gegrüsset, Jesu gütig;* [2] while his last act as a creative musician was to dictate to his son-in-law Altnikol—the old man being then almost totally blind—a chorale prelude on the melody *Wenn wir in höchsten Nöthen sein.*

Some of the preludes were grouped by Bach himself and published during his lifetime. In 1739 he issued the Third Part of the *Clavierübung,* [3] containing twenty chorale arrangements; about 1747-1749 six chorales were published by Schübler, of Zella [4]; while about the same time, in all probability, Balthasar Schmid, of Nuremberg, published the canonic variations on *Vom Himmel hoch da komm ich her.*

Two other collections were grouped by Bach himself, but not published in his lifetime. These were the *Orgelbüchlein,* [5] written, apparently, during the Weimar period (1708-1717) and copied out at Cöthen (1717-1723), and what are usually known as the "Eighteen Great Chorales." These last were revisions,

---

[1] "Partita" in this connection means a set of variations.

[2] Forkel says vaguely that Bach "began to compose" chorale preludes "under the title of *Partite diverse,*" "already when in Arnstadt." Spitta (*Bach,* I., 211) holds that these partitas were written at Lüneburg. They show the influence of Böhm, who was organist at St. John's Church, Lüneburg, from 1698 to his death in 1733. This, of course, does not negate the supposition that they may have been composed after Bach had left Lüneburg. He seems to have revised the variations on *Sei gegrüsset, Jesu gütig* in later life.

[3] The title runs thus: *Third Part of the Clavierübung, containing various preludes upon the catechism hymns and others, for the organ: composed for the soul's delectation of amateurs, and more especially of connoisseurs in this style, by Johann Sebastian Bach, Court Composer,* &c., &c.

[4] *Six Chorales of various kinds to be played on an organ with two manuals and pedals, written by Johann Sebastian Bach, Court Composer,* &c., &c. *Published by Joh. Georg Schübler at Zella in the Thuringian Wald. To be had in Leipzig of Herr Capellmeister Bach, of his sons in Berlin and Halle, and of the publisher in Zella.* The volume bears no date, but a clue to the year is given by the reference to the "son in Halle," *i.e.,* Wilhelm Friedemann Bach, who became organist of the Halle Liebfrauenkirche in 1747.

[5] *The Little Organ Book, wherein instruction is given to a beginning organist how to work out a chorale in every style, also to perfect himself in the study of the pedal, this being treated quite obbligato throughout in the chorales herein contained. To the honour of the Lord Most High, and that my neighbour may be taught thereby. Autore Joanne Sebast. Bach,* &c., &c.

---

made in the closing years of his life, of preludes that had probably been written in the Weimar period.

The *Orgelbüchlein* was originally planned to contain one hundred and sixty-four preludes. Each sheet of the manuscript bears the title of a chorale, [6] a single page being allotted to the shorter ones, a double page to the longer. Only forty-five chorales were actually worked out; [7] if the music of one of these went beyond the allotted space, a slip was pasted at the bottom of the page, or use was made of the tablature. Why the remaining hundred and nineteen preludes were not written is not known; Schweitzer conjectures that Bach picked out "those of which the strong pictorial or characteristic quality seemed to make them specially suitable for music. The texts of the numbers not completed lack these musical qualities. No characteristic theme could be evolved from them; they could only be developed as pure music, not in their poetic or pictorial aspects." Schweitzer's opinion, supported as it is by a certain kind of evidence, will weigh with all students of Bach. Nevertheless it must be observed that many of the untouched chorales are strong in poetic or pictorial qualities, or in both, and some of them have in fact been poetically and pictorially treated by Bach himself in other chorale preludes—*Valet will ich dir geben,* for example. And nothing is more certain than that Bach, when he chose, could give the profoundest poetic import either to words or to a musical device that on the surface seem to be very remote from poetry. See, for instance, what poignancy he has invoked from the canonic form in the *Christe, du Lamm Gottes* in the small space of sixteen bars. We must assume, too, that he knew his own predominant cast of thought, and that at the time he planned out the complete series, selecting his hymns from a vast number of texts applicable to the church seasons he was illustrating, he saw his way to give the needed poetic or pictorial touch to each of them. The fact must not be overlooked that he apparently began work on the series systematically from the first page, and that only in the later stages do big gaps appear between the completed chorales. Thus of the first twenty-seven chorales whose titles

---

[6] "Chorale," in this Introduction, always means the melody, while "hymn" means the poem.

[7] *Liebster Jesu, wir sind hier* is set twice (Nos. 35 and 36).

appear in the volume, all were worked out except No. 6 (*Lob sei Gott in des Himmels Thron*). The written and unwritten preludes in the remainder of the book are as under :—

Not written.		Written.	
Nos. 28 to	33	Nos. 34 to	39
40 to	43		44
45 to	48	49 to	51
52 to	60		61
62 to	64		65
66 to	75	76,	77
78 to	90		91
92 to	97		98
99			100
101 to	112		113
114 to	130		131
132 to	164		

It is highly improbable that in the collection Bach had made of a hundred and sixty-four chorales, of which, according to Schweitzer, only forty-five had the poetic or pictorial qualities he desired, more than half of the chorales exhibiting these qualities should chance to fall within the first twenty-seven of the selection, only thirteen among the last hundred and twenty-five, only two among the last sixty-five, and none at all among the last thirty-three. To suppose this is to allow too much to hazard even in this incalculable world.

In all previous editions of the chorale preludes, except that of the Bachgesellschaft, the works have been arranged, for convenience of reference, in alphabetical order: the unity of the *Orgelbüchlein* has been preserved, but there too the alphabetical order has always been adopted. But the order given by Bach to the chorales of the *Orgelbüchlein* and the *Clavierübung* was in neither case an arbitrary one; and to destroy this order is to disrupt the psychological thread that bound the chorales together in Bach's imagination.

In the German Protestant church the great majority of hymns were, and indeed still are, inseparately associated with this or that period of the church year, or even with some particular Sunday. In the *Orgelbüchlein*, Bach—in this only conforming to a practice that was general among the organists of his time—has planned a series of chorales covering each of the main church periods in turn, thus:—

Advent :   Nos. 1—4.[a]
Christmas : Nos. 5—11.

> (No. 12, *Jesu, meine Freude*, is a *Jesus-Lied*—a hymn of love and adoration of the Saviour.)

Nos. 13, 14.

New Year :   Nos. 15, 16.

> (No. 17, *In dir ist Freude*, is a *Jesus-Lied*.)
>
> (Nos. 18, *Mit Fried und Freud' ich fahr dahin* (the Song of Simeon) and 19, *Herr Gott, nun schleuss den Himmel auf*, are hymns for the dying.)

The Passion : Nos. 20—26.
Easter :   Nos. 27—32.

> (The preludes on the Ascension hymns, that were marked out to follow No. 32, were not composed.)[b]

Pentecost :   No. 33.

> (No. 34, *Herr Jesu Christ, dich zu uns wend*, is a prayer for grace and the strengthening of belief.)

No. 35, *Liebster Jesu, wir sind hier*, which is also set as No. 36, is a baptism hymn.

No. 37, *Dies sind die heil'gen zehn Gebot*—the ten commandments—needs no explanation; nor does

No. 38, *Vater unser im Himmelreich*—the German *Paternoster*.

No. 39, *Durch Adams Fall ist ganz verderbt*, is a hymn "on the fall of man and his blessed salvation through Christ alone."

No. 40, *Es ist das Heil uns kommen her*, is a hymn "of the justification before God through faith, without the merit of works."

No. 41, *Ich ruf' zu dir, Herr Jesu Christ*, is a hymn of supplication for faith, hope and charity.

No. 42, *In dich hab' ich gehoffet, Herr*, is a prayer for protection in bodily and spiritual need.

---

[a] These numbers refer to the *completed* preludes as they appear in the present edition of the *Orgelbüchlein*.

[b] Unless we hold that No. 32, *Heut triumphiret Gottes Sohn*, was intended by Bach for Ascension Sunday. This is really an Easter hymn; but Spitta (II. 270) tells us that it was also one of the hymns "specially appointed" for Ascension in the Saxon Church Service. The chorale immediately preceding it in the *Orgelbüchlein—Erschienen ist der herrliche Tag*—is for Easter; the two immediately following it in the original manuscript, though they were not composed—*Gen Himmel aufgefahren ist* and *Nun freut euch, Gottes Kinder, all*—are for Ascension. *Heut triumphiret Gottes Sohn* may therefore have been associated by Bach, when writing the *Orgelbüchlein*, with either of these feasts. In the book of chorales that accompanies the present edition of the preludes, the hymn is included under Ascension. This grouping certainly has the merit of making Bach's scheme for a musical illustration of the great Festivals of the church year complete; but in the absence of more conclusive evidence than is yet available, the present writer does not feel justified in definitely asserting that such was Bach's intention. The hymn is accordingly grouped here in accordance with the predominantly Easter character of its words. The matter is further discussed in the *Musical Times* for April, 1916.

Pentecost: No. 33—*contd.*

No. 43, *Wenn wir in höchsten Nöthen sein*, is a prayer for help in trouble.

No. 44, *Wer nur den lieben Gott lässt walten*, is a hymn of faith in God's Providence.

No. 45, *Alle Menschen müssen sterben*, is a hymn for the dying, expressing joy in eternal life.

No. 46, *Ach wie nichtig, ach wie flüchtig*, is a hymn for the dying, expressing the vanity of human life.

It will be seen that Bach selected the earlier hymns of the *Orgelbüchlein* in accordance with a scheme that was designed to embrace, in their proper order, Advent, Christmas, the Passion, Easter, the Ascension, and Pentecost. Afterwards the hymns—both those that were worked up into preludes and those that were not—are taken apparently at random from the hymn books. Had Bach really a definite poetic or religious purpose in the later portion of the book, as he indubitably had in the earlier; and if so, what was this purpose?[10]

The basic idea of the collection in the Third Part of the *Clavierübung* admits of no doubt. The chorales are based on the "catechism hymns," that embody the articles of the Lutheran faith; to these are prefixed the *Kyrie*, the *Gloria*, and the hymn to the Trinity, *Allein Gott in der Höh sei Ehr*. With the exception of the last-named, each chorale is made the subject of a larger and a smaller prelude, corresponding to Luther's greater and smaller catechism. "In the former," says Schweitzer, Luther "demonstrates the essence of the faith; in the latter he addresses himself to the children." The larger chorale preludes "are dominated by a sublime musical mysticism, aiming simply at illustrating the central idea of the dogma contained in the words; the smaller ones are of bewitching simplicity." The collection is prefaced by a prelude in E flat, and ends with a triple fugue in the same key.

It is strange that the German editors of the chorale preludes, intimately acquainted as they must have been with the church music and the church ordinances of their race, should have failed to see and to respect Bach's purpose in the groupings of the *Orgelbüchlein* and the *Clavierübung* preludes. Griepenkerl, who edited the Peters edition in 1846, blandly remarks in his preface that "as Bach himself attached no importance to the order of succession of the preludes, we have permitted ourselves to re-arrange them alphabetically, for convenience of reference." In the present edition the chorales of the two collections are printed in the order assigned to them by Bach. The unity of the Schübler chorales and of the eighteen great chorales is also retained, though no poetic or other significance attaches to the order of these.

In the case of the miscellaneous preludes, the alphabetical arrangement is of course the most rational one.

---

[10] On the subject of the scheme of the *Orgelbüchlein* see also Schweitzer, *J. S. Bach*, I., 285 ff.

II.

Of all Bach's works the chorale preludes are probably the least known, even to organists. The reason is not far to seek; unless the study of them is approached along the proper roads, there is a good deal in them that will refuse to yield up its full secret. For a clear understanding of them on the purely musical side two things are necessary—a knowledge of the chorales on which they are based, and a grasp of the structural forms embodied in the preludes. The first of these pre-requisites is now provided in the volume of chorales that accompanies this edition—the harmonisations being mostly by Bach himself. Unless each melodic line of the original is clearly fixed in the mind it is impossible to follow intelligently Bach's treatment of the chorale; especially when he converts the simple line into a far-flung, sinuous arabesque, as in the *O Mensch, bewein' dein' Sünde gross*, is it necessary to keep the plain stem constantly in view.

The forms of the preludes, given a knowledge of the thematic material of these, are theoretically simple enough. The chorale prelude is in essence merely another manifestation of that principle of variation that may almost be said to be two-thirds of the art of musical composition. For nearly as long as organised music goes back we see composers taking secular or sacred melodies as the starting-points for their own works. The older masses and motetts are full of instances of this practice. In the Germany of the early seventeenth century the chorale was not only the centre of the Protestant worship but the expression of the very soul of the German community. It was a time when organ building and organ technique were both rapidly developing. The organist was irresistibly driven into embroidering the chorale with fancies of his own, either in the way of new harmonies during the actual singing of it by choir and congregation, or in the way of thematic manipulation and transformation. Out of the latter mode of treatment came the chorale prelude. In a polyphonic age it was inevitable that composers should see in these well-known melodies inexhaustible material both for fugal movements and for the melodic "colouring,"—*i.e.*, the festooning of the plain melodic stem with fanciful ornamentation—that had such a fascination for many of the minds of the period. By Bach's time all the main lines on which it is possible to treat the organ chorale had long been known and pursued. He could do no more than take up the forms of his predecessors and contemporaries, and, as usual with him, turn them to uses more splendid than could ever have entered into their dreams.

Spitta and others have attempted to classify Bach's chorale preludes and to give each group a definite descriptive title. Rigid nomenclature is of little avail, however, for the various types incessantly melt into each other. The subject is too large to be dealt with here in full; the student will find a lucid historical and æsthetic summary of it in Schweitzer (Eng. trans. Vol. I., Chap. v.), and much valuable information can be dug out of the obscure and badly arranged but indispensable pages of Spitta. The partitas or series of variations constitute a class that requires no explanation; nor need anything but passing mention be made of what, strictly speaking, are not chorale preludes, but merely harmonised versions of the chorales for the church service,—such as *Gelobet seist du, Jesu Christ* (XVIII. 37),[11] *Lobt Gott ihr Christen allzugleich* (XVIII. 74), *Vom Himmel hoch da komm ich her* (XIX. 19), and *Wer nur den lieben Gott lässt walten* (XIX. 21, 22).

Sometimes Bach's treatment of the chorale consists simply of a harmonic intensification along with the slightest possible decoration of the melody; it is as if a master painter were to pass his brush over a picture completed by another hand, and with a stroke or two heighten a light here, darken a shadow there, and give a new meaning to a face or cause a new emotion to well forth from a scene. Specimens of this order of prelude will be seen in *Herzlich thut mich verlangen* (XVIII. 53), *Liebster Jesu wir sind hier* (XVIII. 70), and *Ich ruf zu dir, Herr Jesu Christ* (XV. 111).

From the prelude of this type, as will be seen, polyphonic treatment is wholly absent. But of a great number of preludes polyphony is the life and soul; and this polyphony assumes various forms. From the very first an instinct of formal coherence had impelled organists, when preludising upon a chorale, to derive the thematic material for the prelude from the chorale melody itself. In this way there developed one of the forms most frequently met with in this order of composition,—a prelude in which the familiar chorale melody was painted in large notes, as it were, upon a background built up out of fragments of itself. Sometimes the derived theme would be treated quasi-fugally, as in Pachelbel's prelude upon *Vater unser im Himmelreich*:—

No. 1.   CHORALE:

Sometimes the accompaniment figure would make only a pretence of working out the theme in diminution, and after the first few notes would branch

off into figuration, as in the following arrangement of *Jesus Christus unser Heiland* by Pachelbel:—

No. 2.   CHORALE

This is a form that may easily run to dryness and stiffness. It does so very frequently in the hands of Pachelbel and his fellows, and now and then even in the hands of Bach. The latter treats the form in a variety of ways. Sometimes a fugue will be made out of the first line only of the chorale, as in the *Dies sind die heilgen zehn Gebot*, the *Wir glauben all' an einen Gott*, and the *Jesus Christus unser Heiland* of the *Clavierübung* (XVI. 47, 52, 80). This form has a self-justifying unity. Rather less convincing—for there is a touch of arbitrariness about it— is the form that weaves merely the first two lines of the chorale into a fugue. An example of this is the *Allein Gott in der Höh sei Ehr* (XVI. 41). The method of making a fughetta out of each line of the melody in turn, as in the double pedal *Aus tiefer Noth* of the *Clavierübung* (XVI. 68), inevitably has something over-precise and square-toed about it, to which it sometimes requires all the genius of a Bach to reconcile us. When a long chorale like *Komm, heiliger Geist, Herre Gott* (XVII. 10), of which the stanza contains no less than eight lines and a couple of alleluias, is worked out fugally line by line, the result is a composition excessively long and loosely knit. Before the last of its two hundred bars has been reached we have completely lost touch with the earlier lines of the chorale.

Leaving this style for a moment, let us look at the method that relies mainly on an arabesque treatment of the melody of the chorale, over simple harmonies that knit the arabesque firmly together and establish the connection with the original chorale. A simple example of this is the *Wenn wir in höchsten Nöthen sein* of the *Orgelbüchlein* (XV. 115). In a more complex variety of the form, the accompaniment has independence and polyphonic life, as in the *Nun komm' der Heiden Heiland* for two claviers and pedal (XVII. 46). Here, it will be observed, the accompaniment begins with the imitative treatment of a figure derived from the opening line of the chorale melody. No attempt is made, however, to treat each successive line of the melody in this way, for the special kind of unity aimed at in this order of prelude would be destroyed by such a piecemeal method. Similarly in the *Allein Gott in der Höh sei Ehr* (for two claviers and pedal, canto fermo in tenor, XVII. 60), though the treble and the pedal both hint frequently at the melody, the hints are of the freest kind. In another variant of the form (*Allein Gott in der Höh sei Ehr*, for two claviers and pedal, canto fermo in soprano, XVII. 56), the accompaniment is not derived in any way from the chorale.

The two broad types described in the two preceding paragraphs are seen blended in such a prelude as the exquisite *Schmücke dich, o liebe Seele* (XVII. 22). Here the canto fermo blossoms into the most floreate arabesque, while the accompaniment also is formed out of the chorale melody. This latter is not worked out line by line in the accompaniment, as in the stiffer Pachelbel style, but generates a continuous tissue that always obviously relates to the chorale, yet has a paradoxical independence of it. In the two beautiful settings of *An Wasserflüssen Babylon* (XVII. 18, XVIII. 13), again, the accompaniment is a self-sufficing tone-piece, with a haunting quasi-"motive" running through it. The form of these chorales is perfect, the closest tissue-weaving going hand in hand with the freest outpouring of the poetic imagination. In much the same style is the *Von Gott will ich nicht lassen* (XVII. 43) from the *Eighteen Preludes ;* here the original chorale melody is given out as a canto fermo in the pedal, while several lines of it are also treated floridly in the soprano,[12] and the free accompaniment also derives from the first line of the chorale. This method makes in general for the highest unity of form and spirit ; not only does the canto fermo establish the chorale, but the other parts are incessantly referring to it, and indeed drawing their life from it, yet without any hindrance to their own free evolution. The composer, indeed, is left so free that, as in this case, the latter lines of the chorale can be omitted from the floreate soprano part without any damage being done to the unity of the piece ; the unity of mood is itself sufficient. In another variant of this form, seen in the longer *Vater unser im Himmelreich* of the *Clavierübung* (XVI. 53) the canto fermo appears in canon, against an accompaniment that incessantly works out a florid figure derived from the first line of the chorale alone.

---

[12] Bach's arabesque is often so luxuriant that without a previous knowledge of the chorale the player would hardly suspect the latent existence of the simple theme in the figuration. Bars 17, 18 of *Von Gott will ich nicht lassen*, for example :—

are an elaboration of the third line of the chorale :—

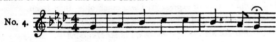

See also the treatment of the first phrase of *Vater unser im Himmelreich* (XVI. 53).

The most perfect unity, again, is the characteristic of the type shown in the great majority of the preludes of the *Orgelbüchlein*. Here the chorale as a living, indivisible entity is taken as the starting point. The main melody flows on uninterruptedly,[13] even though it be luxuriantly figurated, as in *O Mensch, bewein' dein' Sünde gross*. In the *Orgelbüchlein* type, which Bach made peculiarly his own, only two of the melodies besides *O Mensch* are treated in arabesque style,—*Das alte Jahr vergangen ist* and *Wenn wir in höchsten Nöthen sein*. Canon is occasionally used, but none of the chorales are treated on the line-by-line fugal method that came down from Pachelbel. The accompanying figures that support or play about the melody are not derived from the chorale itself,[14] but grow out of the mood of the hymn, or some pictorial image suggested by this, or some definite religious symbol that it evokes.

There remains the form of the pure chorale fantasia, in which the composer launches out into an independent rhapsody inspired by the general mood of the hymn, the chorale melody coming in as a canto fermo later. This type is seen in its perfection in the mighty *Komm, heiliger Geist, Herre Gott* (XVII. 1).

III.

Finally there is the question of the poetic, pictorial and symbolical in the chorale preludes. It has long been recognised that frequently at the back of Bach's mind was some definite verbal or visual conception that accounts for the particular form or colour of his music at a particular point. Spitta was often aware of this, though he was unable or unwilling to see many illustrations of it that are patent enough to us. Long before Spitta, however, this tendency in Bach had been obvious to a few students. Mosewius insists strongly on it in his *J. S. Bach in seinen Kirchenkantaten und Choralgesängen* (1845), though he failed to see that what was true of the vocal music was true of the instrumental works also. Johann Gotthilf Ziegler, one of Bach's pupils, expressly says that his master always urged on him the importance of playing the chorales not merely as music but "according to the tenor of the words."[15] But gradually the sense of the intimate connection between Bach's music and the sentiment of the hymns was lost, so that Weber could actually find fault with certain of Bach's harmonic progressions, not seeing that a passage that was not self-explanatory on the face of it was fully explained and justified by the words that had inspired it.[16]

---

[13] With the solitary exception of *In dir ist Freude*.

[14] With three exceptions—No. 15, *Helft mir Gottes Güte preisen*, No. 37, *Dies sind die heilgen zehn Gebot*, and No. 43, *Wenn wir in höchsten Nöthen sein*. Some people may take the view that the treatment of the pedal in No. 34, *Herr Jesu Christ, dich zu uns wend*, brings that prelude also into this category.

[15] See Spitta I., 524. In face of this it is difficult to agree with Schweitzer (II. 30) that Philipp Emmanuel "had no perception of his father's poetic intentions" in the chorale-movements of the cantatas and Passions.

[16] See Schweitzer II., 30, 31.

It is mainly to Schweitzer[17] and André Pirro[18] that we owe our present knowledge of the extraordinary partiality of Bach for poetic suggestion and pictorial illustration. That he frequently varied the harmonisation of a chorale in a Passion or a cantata according to the words had long been evident to students. Schweitzer and Pirro, however, have further shewn the existence in Bach's music of a number of "motives"—of joy, grief, and so on—and a number of pictorial *clichés*, that always recur in much the same form whenever the words indicate the same image. A knowledge of these is indispensable to the student of the chorale preludes.

His manner of emotional intensification by harmonic means is familiar to every one from his varied harmonisations of the chorale *Herzlich thut mich verlangen* in the Matthew Passion. A less familiar example may be cited in connection with the chorale *Ach Gott und Herr*. With nothing in his mind but the general tenor of the hymn, Bach harmonises the final line of the first verse thus:—[19]

But when he is setting the fourth verse of the hymn in the cantata *Ich elender Mensch*,[20] the idea of penance for sin draws from him these poignant harmonies:—[21]

Of the same order are the expressive harmonies at the end of *O Mensch, bewein' dein' Sünde gross*,—apparently motived by the thought of the

Passion—and in many other of the chorales. For fuller light upon the poetic and pictorial symbolism of the preludes the student must be referred to Schweitzer; here space permits only of the pointing out of some of the most familiar examples, such as the dragging syncopations in *Da Jesus an dem Kreuze stund* (XV. 67), suggested by the weariness of Christ, the wailing chromatics of *O Lamm Gottes* (XV. 58) and *Jesus Christus unser Heiland* (XV. 81), suggested by the Saviour's sufferings,[22] the joy of Simeon in *Mit Fried' und Freud' ich fahr dahin* (XV. 50),[23] and the downward-plunging sevenths, symbolical of the fall of man, in *Durch Adams Fall ist ganz verderbt* (XV. 107).

It has been said in the early part of this Introduction that a full understanding of the chorale preludes is impossible without a knowledge of the original chorale melodies and of Bach's forms. It must now be added that equally indispensable is a knowledge of *the whole* of the words of the hymns. It is not only that Bach "harmonised the poetry" rather than the melodies of the chorales, but that often the title, taken from the first line of the hymn, conveys either no notion of the hymn's general contents or is quite misleading with regard to these. A striking example is *Alle Menschen müssen sterben*. Why, the hearer may ask himself, should Bach be so obviously cheerful at the thought that "all mankind must die"? More than one writer has asked the same question, and been unable to find a satisfactory answer. Mr. Charles Macpherson speaks of the motive of "beatific peace" being "strangely enough" employed in this prelude, though "this is because the last line refers to 'the great glory that is prepared for those who love God'."[24] Spitta, on the other hand,[25] speaks of the "tender melancholy" that lurks in the chorale. But the expression is not one of melancholy but of beatific joy and the reason is that the whole hymn is full of joy. Its text is that mankind dies in order to live eternally, as everything on earth must pass away to be born anew. "Willingly," says the Christian in the second verse, "will I give up this life when it pleases God, for in Jesus' wounds have I found my salvation, and my comfort in the pain of death is the death of Jesus." And in the third verse, "He has purchased my salvation by His death; so I go on my way rejoicing, out of the tumult of this world, to the beautiful heaven of God." And in the sixth, "O Jerusalem, thou beauteous, ah, now lovely is thy light! ah, how sweet sound the songs of praise in thy soft peace! O the joy and rapture." It would indeed be surprising if a musical meditation upon such words as these should breathe anything but beatific joy.

The first line of *Gelobet seist du, Jesu Christ* (Praise be to thee, O Jesu Christ) (XV. 15), again, does not suggest the whole contents of the hymn, which is a

---

[17] *J. S. Bach, Le Musicien-Poète*, 1905, and *J. S. Bach* [a German expansion of the former book], 1908. The latter is now accessible in an English version.

[18] *L'Esthétique de Jean-Sébastien Bach*, 1907.

[19] A translation of the verse is given, along with this particular harmonisation of the chorale, in the collection of chorales that forms a companion to this edition of the preludes.

[20] "If indeed it must be that chastisement and pain must follow upon sin, then . . . . let me bear my penance."

[21] In the *Cowley Carol Book* this setting of Bach's is incongruously linked to the cheery words of a Christmas carol!

[22] The device of using chromatics to express grief was much older than Bach.

[23] The hymn is based on the Song of Simeon (Luke ii., 29-32).

[24] *Chorale Preludes, Ancient and Modern*, in *Proceedings of the Musical Association*, 1912-13, p. 163.

[25] I., 599.

tender meditation over the Holy Child in the manger. It is this tenderness that inspires the caressing harmonies, as every one who is acquainted with the varieties of Bach's harmonic idiom will agree. Nor does the title of *Christ lag in Todesbanden* (XV. 79) account for the jubilant quality of the music. The hymn, however, does not dwell upon Christ "lying bound in the chains of death," but upon His triumph over the grave, and the Christian's redemption from sin.

A slight puzzle is presented by the two arrangements of *An Wasserflüssen Babylon*. In this music there is obviously nothing of the sorrow, the home-sickness, of the 137th Psalm. It is just possible that Bach had in his mind an image of the tranquil river, and that he chose to concentrate upon this, to the neglect of the poem as a whole, in a way that was not uncommon with him. But it is at least as likely that he was thinking of the hymn *Ein Lämmlein geht und trägt die Schuld* ("A Lamb bears the guilt"), that was often sung to the melody of *An Wasserflüssen Babylon*. This is a hymn of tranquil happiness in and gratitude for the Saviour's sacrifice. This cross-fertilisation, as we might call it, of a particular melody by the words of another hymn is familiar to us from the case of the final setting of *Wenn wir in höchsten Nöthen sind*, at the head of which the almost dying composer asked Altnikol to write the title of another hymn, *Vor deinen Thron tret' ich allhier*.

The music of *Das alte Jahr vergangen ist* exhales the very soul of sorrow; but the hymn itself is one of hope for the new year. Bach, however, preferred to dwell upon the melancholy of the dying year, for no better reason, perhaps,—though that is all-sufficient !—than that he happened to be in a melancholy mood at the moment. He chose also to interpret *Durch Adams Fall ist ganz verderbt* more seriously than is justified by the hymn itself, which is really a song of hope and trust. No doubt Bach, like many a modern song-writer, sometimes did not so much make the words of a poem the starting-point for music as pour out upon the words an emotion that was already bursting for an outlet in him.[26] He exercised the privilege of genius to deal as he chose with the emotional possibilities of the chorale and the hymn, no less than with the form of his music.

It is along the converging lines of the poetry and the music of these preludes that the reverent student of them will work. The closer his familiarity with them, the more he will be amazed both at the emotional heights and depths of this great nature and at the incomparable skill and resource of the musician. "With this key," said Wordsworth of the sonnet, "Shakespeare unlocked his heart." The chorale preludes are the key to the very heart of Bach. If everything else of his were lost, from them we could reconstruct him in all his pathos and almost all his grandeur.

ERNEST NEWMAN.

---

[26] Strauss has confessed that this is how some of his own songs came to be written. See the present writer's *Richard Strauss*, p. 94.

EXPLANATION OF THE VARIOUS ORNAMENT SIGNS TO BE FOUND IN BACH'S CHORALE PRELUDES.

THE notes forming these ornaments should always be diatonic (*i.e.*, according to the key of the music), the seventh note of the minor scale being understood as the *leading note*.

(1.) *Triller* (long shake) **Played.**

The *Triller* should generally begin with the accessory note, as given above.

The actual number of repercussions of the shake is left much to the discretion of the performer, and depends upon the length of the note shaken upon and the pace of the music.

When closing-notes are required to the shake they are generally either printed out in full or expressed by means of an affix to the sign

When no closing-notes are indicated, and the note to be shaken is followed by a dot the shake should generally end at the dot,

thus or, more strictly speaking, where the dot itself will admit of being somewhat exaggerated, according to the traditional use of Bach's time, thus

A long shake is sometimes expressed by the signs ᷈ or *tr.* (see under *Prall-triller*).

(2.) *Prall-triller* (transient shake) **Played.**

When the main note of the *Prall-triller* has been preceded by the same note the ornament should begin with the accessory in this manner

Owing to some considerable confusion of the signs *tr.* ᷈ and ᷈ in the various important printed editions of Bach's works, and the apparent inconsistency of the composer himself in the matter of notating shakes, it is doubtful in a number of cases whether the sign ᷈ stands for a *Prall-triller* or a *Triller* (long shake). Sometimes the context will be found helpful in giving a solution of the difficulty. For instance, when the closing notes are given a shake is probably intended, and the same may generally be taken as correct when the sign appears over the leading note in a cadence:

Played.

In other cases the player must rely upon his judgment. The chapter on Bach in Dannreuther's "Musical Ornamentation" (Part I., pp. 161-210)* gives a very detailed explanation of the use of shakes and other ornaments under various conditions.

(3.) Mordent (short) **Played.**

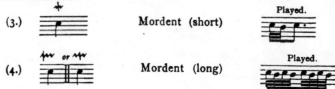

(4.) Mordent (long) **Played.**

These signs should not be confused with that representing a *Triller* with closing notes ᷈.

* Novello & Co.

(5.) *Triller*, with prefix from above.

Played.

The number of repercussions of the shake being according to circumstances, as before.

(6.) *Triller*, with prefix from below.

Played.

(7.) *Triller*, with prefix from above, and closing notes.

• Played

(8.) *Triller*, with prefix from below, and closing notes.

• Played

(a) Above a note.

(9.) *Doppelschlag* (Turn).

Played.

(b) Between two notes.

" " Played.

(c) Over a dot.

" " Played.

(10.) From above. *Vorschlag* (Appoggiatura).

Played. † or

(11.) From below.

" " Played. † or

---

* These Groups, and a few others in this "Explanation," must be regarded as an approximate general effect, and not as a strict representation of the time-value of a crotchet.

† The longer form is that given by Bach himself in his "*Explication* of various signs," written for the "Clavierbüchlein."

Many of the signs for the *Vorschlag* have been replaced in printed editions by small notes, the time-value of which often leaves room for doubt as to the exact manner of their performance. Hence there is sometimes a difference of opinion among Bach authorities as to how certain of them should be played.

Common sense, combined with a study of the context, must be relied upon as the best guide in the matter.

Dannreuther gives a detailed expression of his own views regarding Bach's *Appoggiature* (which are those accepted by many other eminent musicians) in his "Musical Ornamentation."

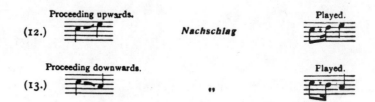

(12.) Proceeding upwards.   *Nachschlag*   Played.

(13.) Proceeding downwards.   "   Played.

Opening of Chorale Prelude, "Allein Gott in der Höh' sei Ehr'" (XVII., 56).

• *Nachschlag*.   † *Vorschlag*

Played.

(14.) *Triller*, preceded by *Appoggiatura*.   Played.

(15.) *Schleifer* (Slide).   Played.

JOHN E. WEST.

CONTENTS.

THE SIX "SCHÜBLER' CHORALE PRELUDES.

THE "CLAVIERÜBUNG," PART III.

Wachet auf, ruft uns die Stimme.

Edited by John E. West.

(rit.)

Wo soll ich fliehen hin

or

Auf meinen lieben Gott.

Edited by John Pointer.

BWV 646

Wer nur den lieben Gott lässt walten.

Edited by John Pointer.

BWV 647

Meine Seele erhebt den Herren.

Edited by John E. West

BWV 648

Ach bleib bei uns, Herr Jesu Christ.

Edited by John E. West.

BWV 649

Kommst du nun, Jesu, vom Himmel herunter.

Edited by John E. West.

BWV 650

18

13885

Prelude in E♭ major.

"Pro Organo pleno."

BWV 552

Praeludium pro Organo pleno

(a) Kyrie, Gott Vater in Ewigkeit.

Edited by John E. West.

Edited by John E. West.

(b) Christe, aller Welt Trost.

13885

(c) # Kyrie, Gott heiliger Geist.

Edited by John E. West.

F

(a) Kyrie, Gott Vater in Ewigkeit.

Alio modo.

Edited by John E. West.

(b) Christe, aller Welt Trost.

Edited by John E.West.

Edited by John E. West.

(c) Kyrie, Gott heiliger Geist.

BWV 674

Allein Gott in der Höh' sei Ehr.'

(Canto fermo in Alto.)

BWV 675

Edited by John E. West.

13885

(rall.)

Allein Gott in der Höh' sei Ehr.'

Edited by John E. West.

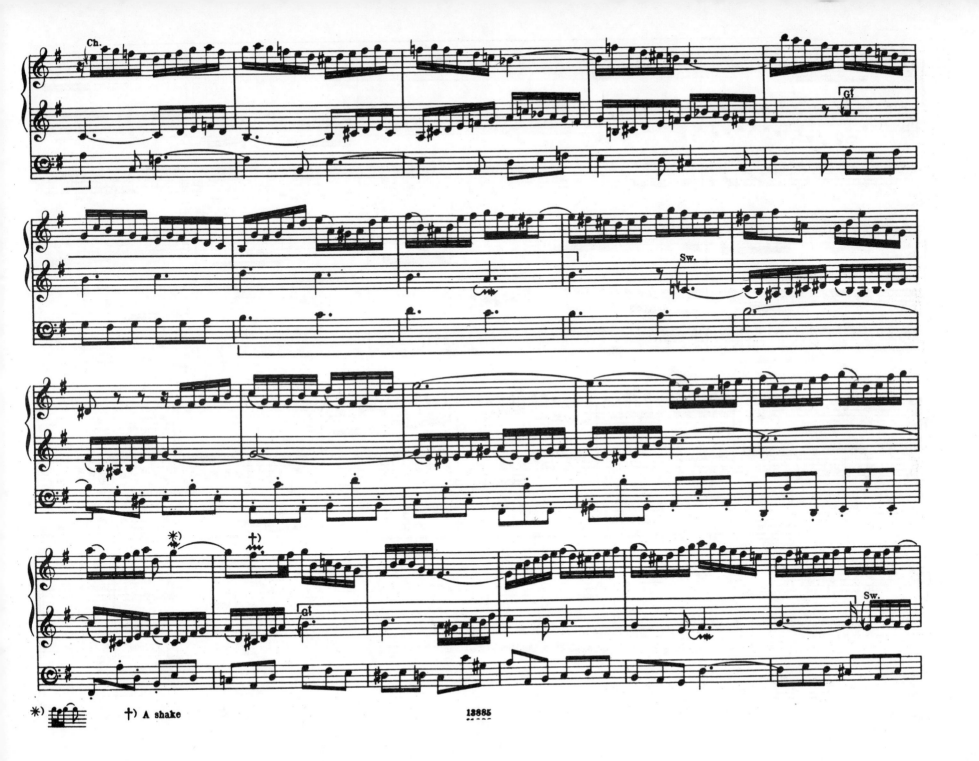

*) ♪♪♪ 𝄐   †) A shake

Allein Gott in der Höh' sei Ehr.'
(FUGHETTA.)

Edited by John E. West.

Dies sind die heil'gen zehn Gebot'.

Edited by John E. West.

BWV 678

18885

H

Dies sind die heil'gen zehn Gebot'.

(FUGHETTA.)

BWV 679

Edited by John E. West.

Wir glauben all' an einen Gott, Schöpfer—

"In Organo pleno."

BWV 680

Edited by J. F. Bridge and James Higgs.

13885

Wir glauben all' an einen Gott, Schöpfer—

(FUGHETTA.)

Edited by John E. West.

BWV 681

Vater unser im Himmelreich.

Edited by John E. West.

K.

Vater unser im Himmelreich.

(Alio modo.)

Edited by John E. West.

Poco Allegretto. ♪ = 126.

MANUAL.

13885

Christ, unser Herr, zum Jordan kam.

(a) Choir or Swell, 8 & 4 ft (b) Great, soft 8 ft (c) Pedal, Solo, 4 ft

Edited by J. F. Bridge and James Higgs.

BWV 684

Canto fermo in Pedal.

64

Christ unser Herr zum Jordan kam.
(Alio modo.)

BWV 685

Edited by John E. West.

13885

Aus tiefer Noth schrei' ich zu dir.

Con Pedale doppio.

Edited by John E. West.

BWV 686

13885

Aus tiefer Noth schrei' ich zu dir.

(Alio modo.)

Edited by John E. West.

BWV 687

Jesus Christus unser Heiland.

Edited by John E. West.

BWV 688

Jesus Christus unser Heiland.
(FUGUE.)

Edited by John E. West.

BWV 689

MANUAL.

Fuga â 5 con pedale pro Organo pleno

BWV 552

13885

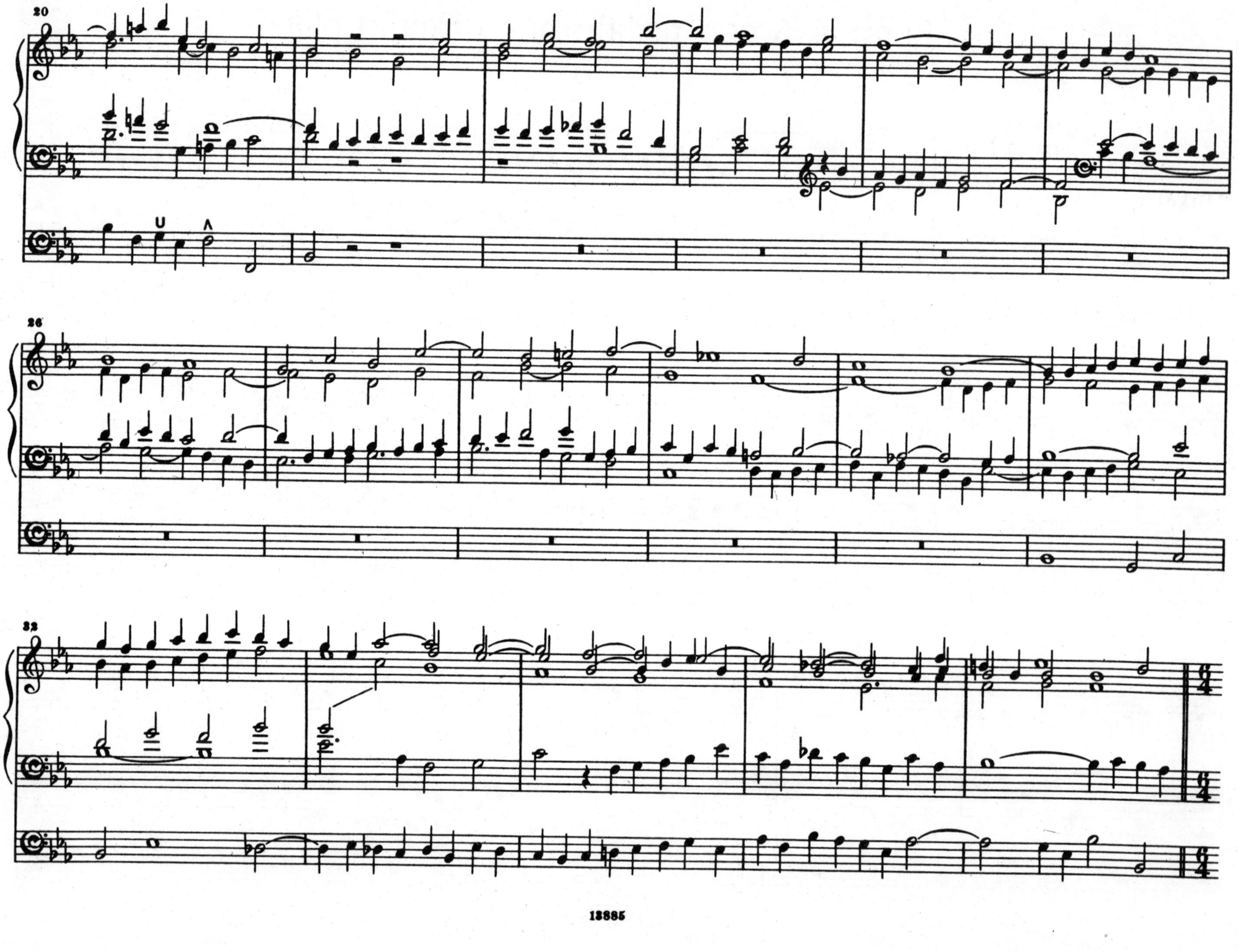

THE ORGAN WORKS OF J. S. BACH

BOOKS I, IV, V EDITED BY JOHN DYKES BOWER AND WALTER EMERY

BOOKS II, III, VI TO XII EDITED BY SIR FREDERICK BRIDGE AND JAMES HIGGS   BOOKS XV TO XX EDITED BY SIR IVOR ATKINS AND OTHERS

(The BWV numbers according to Schmieder's Thematic Index are given in brackets)

BOOK I
EIGHT SHORT PRELUDES AND FUGUES (553-560)

BOOK II   MISCELLANEOUS
Allabreve in D major (589)
Prelude in G major (568)
Canzona in D minor (588)
'Giant' Fugue in D minor (Prelude on *Wir glauben all'
    an einen Gott, Schöpfer*) (680)
Fugue in G minor (arranged from Cantata No. 131)
    (131a)
'Little' Prelude and Fugue in E minor (533)
Prelude and Fugue in C minor (549)
Trio in D minor (583)

BOOK III   MISCELLANEOUS
Five-part Fantasia in C minor (562)
Fugue in B minor on a subject by Corelli (579)
Prelude and Fugue in A major (536)
'Short' Prelude and Fugue in C major (545)
Fantasia and Fugue in C minor (537)
'Little' Fugue in G minor (578)

BOOK IV
SONATAS FOR TWO MANUALS AND PEDALS
(Nos. I—III) (525-527)

BOOK V
SONATAS FOR TWO MANUALS AND PEDALS
(Nos. IV—VI) (528-530)

BOOK VI   MISCELLANEOUS
Toccata and Fugue in D minor (565)
Prelude and Fugue in D major (532)
Prelude and Fugue in F minor (534)
Prelude and 'St. Anne' Fugue in E flat (552)

BOOK VII   MISCELLANEOUS
'Great' Prelude and Fugue in A minor (543)
'Great' Prelude and Fugue in B minor (544)
'Great' Prelude and Fugue in C minor (546)
Prelude and Fugue in C major (531)
Prelude and Fugue in G major (550)

BOOK VIII   MISCELLANEOUS
Toccata in C (or E). (566)
Prelude and 'Wedge' Fugue in E minor (548)
'Great' Prelude and Fugue in G major (541)
Prelude and Fugue in G minor (535)
Fantasia and Fugue in G minor (the 'Great' G minor)
    (542)

BOOK IX   MISCELLANEOUS
Toccata in C major (564)
Prelude and 'Fiddle' Fugue in D minor (539)
'Great' Prelude and Fugue in C major (547)
Fantasia in G major (572)
Toccata and Fugue in F major (540)

BOOK X   MISCELLANEOUS
'Dorian' Toccata and Fugue in D minor (538)
Prelude and Fugue in A minor (551)
Passacaglia and Fugue in C minor (582)
Fugue in C minor on a subject by Legrenzi (574)
Prelude in A minor (569)

BOOK XI   FOUR CONCERTOS
(Arrangements of Violin Concertos by Antonio Vivaldi)
Concerto No. 1 in G major (592)
Concerto No. 2 in A minor (593)
Concerto No. 3 in C major (594)
Concerto No. 4 in C major (595)

BOOK XII   MISCELLANEOUS
'Jig' Fugue in G major (577)
Fantasia and Fugue in A minor (561)
Fantasia, with imitation, in B minor (563)
Fantasia in G major (571)
Fugue in D major (580)
Fugue in G major (576)
Prelude in C major (567)
Fantasia in C major (570)
Prelude in C major (943)
Fugue in C minor (575)
Fugue in C major (946)
Pastorale (590)
Trio in C minor (585)
Aria in F (587)

BOOKS XIII and XIV
discontinued. They contained selected Chorale Preludes
which are also to be found in Books XV to XIX.

BOOK XV   ORGELBÜCHLEIN
(The Little Organ Book)

BOOK XVI
THE SIX 'SCHÜBLER' CHORALE PRELUDES AND PART III OF
THE CLAVIERÜBUNG

BOOK XVII
THE 'EIGHTEEN' CHORALE PRELUDES

BOOK XVIII
MISCELLANEOUS CHORALE PRELUDES (PART I)

BOOK XIX
MISCELLANEOUS CHORALE PRELUDES (PART II) AND
VARIATIONS

BOOK XX
FOUR-PART HARMONIZATIONS OF THE CHORALES USED IN
THE ORGAN WORKS

NOVELLO

BACH'S ORNAMENTS

Walter Emery

Bach's ornaments are puzzles to most musicians. The same ornament often has alternate readings in different editions, and it is difficult to decide which to choose. The author, by going back to the early textbooks, is able to give great help to the serious musician who wishes to interpret ornaments correctly. They are systematically listed, and the many musical examples show the practice of Bach's own day.

'Whatever may be right or wrong for Purcell, Couperin and others, Mr Emery is a guide for Bach whom every reader of his little manual will learn to trust.'

Eric Blom

DEMY OCTAVO

164 PAGES

69 (1971)